"For Santiago de Barry and his family,
dear friends since the day I was born."

© Text & illustrations: Pau Estrada, 2013

Copyright of portrait of Antoni Gaudí i Cornet: Frederic Ballell/Arxiu Fotogràfic Barcelona.
The other pictures have been taken by Pau Estrada.

Original Title: Un paseo con el señor Gaudí

© EDITORIAL JUVENTUD, S. A., 2013
Provença, 101 - 08029 Barcelona
info@editorialjuventud.es
www.editorialjuventud.es

Translated by Joanna Sands
Revised by Esther Sarfatti

Design and layout: Mercedes Romero

First edition, April 2013
Second edition, June 2013
Third edition, October 2013
Fourth edition, June 2014
Fifth edition, December 2014
Sixth edition, July 2015
Seventh edition, July 2016
Eighth edition, June 2017
Ninth edition, April 2018

ISBN 978-84-261-3986-3

DL B 7790-2013
E. J. Edition Number: 13.626

Printed in Spain
Arts Gràfiques Grinver- Avda. Generalitat, 39
Sant Joan Despí (Barcelona)

A STROLL WITH MR

gaudí

Text & Illustrations
Pau Estrada

Editorial EJ Juventud

Mr Gaudí leaves home early for work, as he does every morning. It's a chilly day. "Brrr!" he utters, as he pulls his hat down over his ears. He warms his hands with his breath, buttons up his jacket and starts to walk.

Antoni Gaudí lives in a pink house in the middle of a park that looks like an enchanted forest made of stone. He goes down the steps that lead to the exit and greets his friend the dragon, the guardian of the park.

"See you later, my dear friend!" he says, raising his hat. "Look after the park until my return. I must hurry. I don't want to be late for work."

The multicoloured dragon replies with a smile to this ritual, which is repeated every morning. Meanwhile, Mr Gaudí quickens his step and walks down to the city.

Like every morning, the streets are bustling. Horse carts are urged on by shouts from their drivers, trams packed full of passengers screech and bicycles fly along at great speed like swallows, negotiating the traffic.

Mr Gaudí walks along, not paying attention. He's rather absentminded and he sometimes bumps into other pedestrians or crosses the road without looking.

"Careful there! Look where you're going!" shouts a cyclist.

To passersby, Mr Gaudí resembles a white-bearded beggar, lost in thought. Some of them even step out of the way, fearing he might ask them for money.

You'd never imagine that this is Barcelona's most famous architect. Thanks to his imagination, some of the city's most original and emblematic buildings have been created. He has also designed monuments, lampposts, benches, and even paving stones.

Yet today, like every other day, he goes along his way, absorbed in his thoughts. Nobody recognizes the taciturn old man as he walks by.

Mr Gaudí arrives at Casa Milà, an apartment building that he has completed recently. Like all his projects, Casa Milà looks like nothing ever seen before. Resembling an enormous mountain of stone, its curving silhouette looks like something out of a dream or a fairy tale. Nonetheless, many people find this building extremely ugly, claiming that it looks more like a quarry than a block of flats. Thus its nickname, "La Pedrera", which means "quarry" in Catalan.

This morning Mr Gaudí is at Casa Milà trying to calm down some residents who aren't at all happy with their new home.

"Look here, Mr Architect," says a lady. "You may be a genius, but with these curved walls and ceilings that look more like a cave than a flat, it's impossible to furnish or hang a picture. And what about my grand piano? It doesn't fit in the music room! Can you tell me where exactly I'm supposed to put my piano?"

"Madame," answers Mr Gaudí with his eyebrows raised, on the verge of losing his patience, "I suggest you try playing the violin!"

After an hour of listening to complaints, the old architect's
head is about to explode and he goes up to the roof terrace for a bit
of air. He breathes deeply and sits down on a step.
"People who are so conventional drive me mad!" he murmurs
while he watches the flight of the pigeons in the sky.
"Why is it so difficult for them to let go of their prejudices
and open up their imaginations?"

"Right! Off to work, we've wasted enough time this morning," he says to himself as he gets to his feet.

Mr Gaudí heads out onto the street and starts to walk, munching along on some of the hazelnuts that he normally carries in his pockets.

A few blocks away from Casa Milà, the biggest project of his life is being built: a church called the Sagrada Familia (the Church of the Holy Family). It will be as big as a cathedral and as tall as a skyscraper.

The old architect arrives at the Sagrada Familia
and goes down to the workshop. There, his collaborators
update him on the building's progress. For those who don't
know him well, Mr Gaudí may appear to be the most
difficult and chaotic architect in the world. Rather than
sketching plans on paper, he prefers to illustrate his ideas
with handmade cardboard or plaster sculptures. Sometimes
he sets up models made of cables, ropes, and hanging
weights and uses mirrors to visualize his designs rightside-
up. He often arrives at the work site with new ideas and
changes the project on the spur of the moment, almost
on a whim.

Nonetheless, his assistants, workers and craftsmen,
who have known him for many years, have learned to
interpret his ideas, transforming them into stone, brick,
mosaic or wrought iron until they finally become art.

As evening falls, Mr Gaudí retires to talk to Josep Maria Jujol, one of his closest collaborators. The young architect puts a question to him that has been worrying him for some time.

"Master, the construction of the Sagrada Familia is going well. Soon we'll finish the first towers, but have you considered that it may take many more years to complete this great work? Clearly we won't live to see it finished."

"My dear Jujol, I know who I'm working for, and my client is in no hurry. How do you think the cathedrals of the past were built? The Sagrada Familia is a project that will span several generations, and each one will help to enrich its splendour. While it's true that we can only begin it and allow others to finish it, one day it will be completed and it will be a joy to see. The Sagrada Familia will be the pride of Barcelona, I can assure you."

This evening Mr Gaudí can't linger because he has arranged to have dinner with his friend Count Güell. After giving some final instructions to his colleagues, he puts on his hat and says goodbye.

Rushing off to meet his friend, his head full of ideas, he crosses the road again without looking and has the second near miss of the day.

"Watch where you're going, mister!" shouts a traffic guard.

Dazed, the old architect stammers out an apology, gets onto a tram and heads to the upper quarter of the city.

Count Eusebi Güell is Mr Gaudí's only neighbour in the park where he lives. In fact, Count Güell is the park's owner, and his name is written in large letters in mosaics at the entrance: Park Güell. With his fortune, he has financed many of Mr Gaudí's projects, although he often asks himself if he's not becoming as eccentric as his friend. He sometimes wonders whether the architect's outlandish designs will eventually ruin him.

When they built Park Güell
some years ago, the Count wanted
to create a residential area for the rich,
full of luxury mansions, but nobody
was interested in his idea of a garden
city. Now, just he and Mr Gaudí
live in the solitary park.

Seated on the bench that snakes around the square, the Count lets out a melancholy sigh.

"Antoni, my friend," he says, "we must yield to the evidence that this park will never be what I hoped it would be. Between those who think it's too far from the city centre and those who detest your architecture, of the sixty plots up for sale only one has sold."

"You are right, Don Eusebi." answers
Mr Gaudí. "I'm afraid that you and I are the
only people who like my architecture."
"Well, now, I'm not saying that I love it,
but I certainly respect it." replies
the Count, getting to his feet.

After walking for a while in silence, Count Güell turns to his friend, strokes his beard solemnly and declares: "Let's say no more, Antoni! We're going to forget about the garden city that will never be, and all those rich people who'll never come to live here. I'm tired of seeing this park so empty. This marvellous place wasn't built for two solitary old men like us to live in alone. I've decided that Park Güell should become a public park where children can play, families can enjoy themselves, and everyone who comes to Barcelona can visit."

"An excellent idea, Don Eusebi!" responds Mr Gaudí enthusiastically.

The two friends dine together in the Count's mansion. Whilst Don Eusebi tucks into a feast, Mr Gaudí, a vegetarian, is happy to eat a green salad and some steamed vegetables.

The evening hours quietly pass, and the two friends continue their endless conversation, recalling memories of their youth and imagining new projects that will never come to fruition.

"Just between the two of us, Don Eusebi, do you know what my great dream as an architect is?" says Mr Gaudí with a look of complicity. "I would like to construct a monumental building in New York, the city of skyscrapers. Don't laugh, dear friend, I even have the plans drawn!"

"Ah, America! The New World!" exclaims the Count, a smile lighting up his face as he imagines the land where his father made his fortune many years ago.

It is late when the two friends part. On his way home, Mr Gaudí stops to say goodnight to the multicoloured dragon.

"Here I am, my friend, after another dinner with the Count, trying to put the world to rights, as usual! But we know that our time is coming to an end. One day, in the not too distant future, we'll be history, and you'll still be here guarding the park for the generations to come.

Goodnight, dear dragon. May providence be with you."

The moon and stars shine in the sky above Park Güell, and Mr Gaudí walks towards his house, lost in thought. Imagining new buildings in his head, he designs arches, domes, vaults and columns. However, as he glances up at the full moon, he stops in his footsteps, and the distant memory of a young love that wasn't to be invades his thoughts. For a moment, he seems to feel a pang of melancholy, but he quickly pulls down his hat, quickens his step and enters the doorway. Tomorrow it's back to work and there is so much to be done.

Antoni Gaudí (1852-1926)

Antoni Gaudí i Cornet is one of the most renowned architects of our time, and the great master of Catalan Modernism. He contributed towards creating the image of Barcelona, and every year millions of tourists visit the city to admire places like Park Güell, the Sagrada Familia or Casa Milà.

However, Gaudí wasn't born in Barcelona but in Tarragona. The exact place of his birth is not known, as two towns, Reus and Riudoms, both claim to be his birthplace. Although he was a good student, Gaudí said his best teacher was nature itself, with its infinite variety of textures and geological and botanical forms. Early on, he discovered his vocation for architecture and he moved to Barcelona to study at university, where he quickly began to stand out because of his personality and his original designs. As a young man, Gaudí left no one indifferent, and on the day he graduated, the dean of the faculty of architecture said: "I don't know if we have before us a genius or a madman."

Not long after beginning his professional career, Gaudí got a job that would change his life and to which he would dedicate himself for more than forty years. Midway through the 19th century, a group of devotees decided to build a church that would serve as an "expiatory temple" for the city of Barcelona, but the project progressed very slowly and the original architect was dismissed. Gaudí appeared to be the ideal candidate to continue the work because he was talented as well as very religious. He was to completely transform the project, and would end up creating one of the most original architectural experiments in modern art. The Sagrada Familia is such a huge project that

Antoni Gaudí is born on the 25th of June in Reus or Riudoms (Tarragona).

He completes his degree in architecture.

At the age of 31 he becomes head architect of the Sagrada Familia.

He complete Palau Güell.

| 1852 | 1873 | 1878 | 1883 | 1888 | 1890 |

He begins his studies at the School of Architecture in Barcelona.

He meets Eusebi Güell.

He designs El Capricho in Comillas (Cantabria) and the pavilions of the Finca Güell.

He finishes Casa Vicens and works on the Teresian School in Barcelona.

He designs Casa Botines in León and the Episcopa Palace in As

it is still under construction many years after the death of Gaudí. He, however, was not worried about how long the work would take. As he said, everything in nature, like a centenarian oak, needs time to grow.

Apart from the Sagrada Familia, Gaudí also created many other structures, from apartment buildings to mansions and churches. He also designed lampposts, paving stones, furniture and interiors. He never travelled outside of Spain, and the majority of his work is to be found in Barcelona. Casa Batlló and Casa Milà, two of his most emblematic buildings, are situated on Passeig de Gràcia, Barcelona's main avenue. Gaudí also carried out some work outside of Catalonia, for example the Palace of the Bishop of Astorga, in León, the tower named "El Capricho", in Comillas, Santander, and the restoration of the cathedral of Palma de Mallorca.

Gaudí was an unusual person. He neglected his appearance and wore the same suit everyday until it literally fell to pieces. With his diet and health, however, he was very meticulous: he was strictly vegetarian, ate no salt and didn't smoke or drink alcohol. He never married and had no interest in fame or fortune. His life was dedicated entirely to his work. He was said to be inflexible and stubborn, but he could also be affectionate and had a subtle sense of humour. He was considerate to his collaborators and workers; he always encouraged them to do their very best. His motto was "Festina lente", a Latin phrase that means "more haste, less speed."

Gaudi and Güell in Colonia Güell.

In 1878, Gaudí met Eusebi Güell, a young entrepreneur and the son of one of the country's richest families, who had also received

He goes to live in Park Güell and finishes Casa Batlló.

After finishing the crypt at the Colonia Güell, Gaudí decides to devote himself exclusively to the Sagrada Familia.

Gaudí is run over by a tram on the 7th of June and dies three days later.

| 1900 | 1906 | 1910 | 1915 | 1918 | 1926 |

Construction begins at Park Güell. Gaudí completes Casa Calvet (awarded as best building of the year).

Construction is completed at Casa Milà on Barcelona's Passeig de Gràcia.

Eusebi Güell, his friend and patron, dies.

His funeral is attended by thousands of mourners.

Antoni Gaudí (1852-1926)

the title of count from the King. Their friendship was to last the rest of their lives. Thanks to his personal fortune and his artistic sensitivity, Count Güell became Gaudí's patron. Thus, some of Gaudí's most inspired works, including Palau Güell, Colonia Güell and eventually Park Güell, were born. In Great Britain, Güell had seen the typical garden cities and was captivated by their harmonious combination of nature and urban landscape. In this period, city inhabitants, especially in Barcelona, lived crowded together in inhospitable quarters where disease was rampant. Searching for a healthier way of living, Güell decided to build a garden city on a hill on the outskirts of Barcelona and he commissioned Gaudí with the project, giving him complete artistic freedom.

In Park Güell Gaudí created an extraordinarily original place where he developed some of his most characteristic techniques, for example "trencadís", mosaics made using waste ceramics. In 1904, the park was opened and both Güell and Gaudí went to live there.

However, as a residential estate, Park Güell was a commercial failure as it was far from the city centre and also, even though it may be difficult to believe today, Gaudí's architecture was not popular at the time. For several years, Güell and Gaudí were practically the only residents of the park. The count died in 1916, and Gaudí continued to live in Park Güell until the last year of his life, when he moved to his studio at the Sagrada Familia. He died after being run over by a tram in 1926.

Shortly afterwards, the Güell family donated the park to the city of Barcelona. Today, the house where Gaudí once lived is a museum, and Güell's mansion a primary school.

One hundred years later, and every year on the 12th of February, Saint Eulalia's day (the former patron saint of Barcelona), Gaudí and Güell, the two most popular "cabezudos" (human figures with huge heads) of the Baldiri Reixach school, continue to walk together, parading with the school children.

Author's Note

Picture of the author, Pau Estrada, when he was a child, taken by his father David Estrada Herrero, at Park Güell.

When you have been born and raised in Barcelona, Gaudí becomes an indelible part of your childhood, and for me, Park Güell is almost like my backyard. When I was a young boy, they used to hire out bicycles to children in the park's large square, and it was there that I learnt to ride a bike. I remember one day all the bikes for young children –the ones with stabilisers– were taken, and my mother hired a normal bicycle, one with just two wheels. She assured me that she would hold me, and I began to pedal, even though I was quite scared, All of a sudden I realized that my mother was no longer behind me. I was riding on my own, but instead of losing my balance and falling, I happily kept pedalling. I had just learnt how to ride a bike!

Now that I'm older I continue going to the park to accompany visitors who come to see Barcelona or simply to go up to the highest point and contemplate the view of the city from there. I often ask myself what Park Güell might have been like a hundred years ago, when there were no residents, tourists, or practically any houses around it, and along its avenues strolled two white-bearded old men: Güell and Gaudí. This book is my small tribute to these two people. Thanks to them, today we can enjoy such a unique and inspirational place as Park Güell.

GAUDÍ'S ITINERARY

1 — MR GAUDÍ'S HOUSE IS IN PARK GÜELL. ISN'T IT BEAUTIFUL? TODAY IT'S THE GAUDÍ HOUSE MUSEUM.

2 — THE DRAGON GREETING MR GAUDÍ IS COVERED WITH TILES OF MANY COLOURS. IT'S STILL THERE TODAY, GUARDING THE PARK'S ENTRANCE.

7 — CASA BATLLÓ USED TO BE CALLED THE "HOUSE OF BONES" DUE TO ITS BONE-LIKE COLUMNS AND ITS BALCONIES RESEMBLING SKULLS.

THE CONSTRUCTION OF SAGRADA FAMILIA HAS BEEN LONG AND ARDUOUS. IT IS EXPECTED TO BE FINISHED IN 2026.

6

8

9 — IN PARK GÜELL THERE IS A GREAT HALL SUPPORTED BY COLUMNS. ON ITS CEILING THERE ARE FOUR ROSETTES REPRESENTING THE FOUR SEASONS.

WHEN CASA MILÀ WAS BUILT MANY PEOPLE FOUND IT EXTREMELY UGLY AND GAVE IT ALL SORTS OF FUNNY NICKNAMES, LIKE "LA PEDRERA" ("QUARRY" IN CATALAN).

THE ROOF TERRACE AT CASA MILÀ IS A SCULPTURE GARDEN! THE STAIRCASE EXITS LOOK LIKE MERINGUES AND THE CHIMNEYS LIKE MEDIEVAL WARRIORS.

SAGRADA FAMILIA WAS ALSO KNOWN AS THE "CATHEDRAL FOR THE POOR" AND IT USED TO HAVE A SCHOOL FOR THE WORKERS' CHILDREN.

FROM THE UNDULATING BENCH THAT SURROUNDS THE MAIN SQUARE YOU CAN ENJOY GREAT VIEWS OVER THE CITY OF BARCELONA.

THE TWO HOUSES AT THE ENTRANCE SEEM TO BE MADE OF GINGERBREAD LIKE IN A FAIRY TALE. THE ENTIRE PARK GÜELL IS AN ENCHANTING DREAM WORLD OF FANTASY AND IMAGINATION.